C000244405

SNUFKIN'S
book of thoughts

ILLUSTRATIONS AND QUOTATIONS BY TOVE JANSSON
TEXT BY SAMI MALILA
TRANSLATION BY PAMELA KASKINEN

SELF
MADE
HERO

Excerpts and illustrations by Tove Jansson © Moomin Characters Ltd., Finland
Text © Sami Malila and WSOY
Original title: "Nuuskamuikkusen mietekirja"
First published in Finnish by Werner Söderström Corporation (WSOY) in 2006,
Helsinki, Finland
Translation into English © Pamela Kaskinen
First published in English by SelfMadeHero in 2010
A division of Metro Media Ltd
5 Upper Wimpole Street London W1G 6BP
www.selfmadehero.com

Publishing Director: Emma Hayley
Marketing Director: Doug Wallace
Layout designer: Kurt Young
With thanks to: Nick de Somogyi and Jane Laporte

This work has been published with the financial assistance of
FILI – Finnish Literature Exchange

FINNISH LITERATURE EXCHANGE

All rights reserved. No portion of this book may be reproduced, stored in a retrieval system,
or transmitted in any form or by any means, mechanical, electronic, photocopying, recording,
or otherwise, without written permission from the publisher.

A CIP record for this book is available from the British Library

978-1-906838-21-8

10 9 8 7 6 5 4 3 2

Printed and bound in England

To the Reader

The beloved Moomin stories of
Tove Jansson are full of thrilling
adventures, exuberant humour, eternal
truths and timeless wisdom.

Snufkin lives his life in his own peaceful
way. To Moomintroll, he is an irreplaceable
friend and all the other residents of
Moominvalley look to him for counsel.

We hope you enjoy the wise words and
enchanting insights of
Snufkin's Book of Thoughts!

*Excerpts and illustrations are from the following WSOY editions of
the Moomin books, translated from the original Swedish into Finnish:*

MUUMIPEIKKO JA PYRSTÖTÄHTI

TAIKURIN HATTU

VAARALLINEN JUHANNUS

TAIKATALVI

NÄKYMÄTÖN LAPSI JA MUITA KERTOMUKSIA

MUUMIPAPAN UROTYÖT

MUUMIPAPPA JA MERI

MUUMILAAKSON MARRASKUU

Contents

Radiant Mornings and Peaceful Nights

SNUFKIN woke up quickly, his eyes and ears alert.

"TODAY we must do something very special, for it will be a glorious day."

"THIS place is beautiful," said Snufkin. "Just look at the black velvet tree with the mass of silver colours beyond. And look at the mountains off in the distance that shimmer violet and red!"

SNUFKIN still hadn't returned home. On nights like these, he liked to wander about by himself with his harmonica. Yet there was no singing tonight; he must have been off exploring.

A new moon rose over the tips of the trees and Snufkin stood admiring it. He was completely transfixed.

"I ought to make a wish," he thought. "In honour of the new moon."

THE adventures of the previous night were now just a memory and a new summer day stretched out long before them. They swam like porpoises through the waves and rode the crests back to shore. Sniff was playing in the shallow water. Snufkin was further out, floating on his back and looking at the sky, all blue and golden.

Thoughts about the Sea
and the Forest

"IF you come shortly after midday, the Hemulen and I could go out sailing."

SNUFKIN sat down with his head in his hands and lamented, "The beautiful sea! Gone! Destroyed! No more sailing, no more swimming, no more giant pike! No great storms, no shining ice, no gleaming surface at night to reflect the stars…" He put his head against his knee and refused to look up again.

"THERE'S going to be a thunderstorm, in any case,"
said Snufkin.

THE thunder sounded much closer now.

"I'll go and watch the weather from the peninsula," said Snufkin. He pulled his hat down hard over his ears and left. Alone and content, he strolled out to the farthest point and sat himself down with his back against a large rock.

SNUFKIN jumped up and down with joy and admiration.

"This is incredible weather!" thought Snufkin. "I wonder where the lightning struck."

Snufkin had barely cast off when the dragon came flying towards him and settled on his knee. It was literally purring with pleasure that it had found Snufkin once again.

"Shoo! Be off with you. Go home!" he said.

Sniff yawned. "Shall we go hunting for bats?" he suggested.

"Yes, let's go!" said Snufkin.

On Serenity, Peace
and Beauty

"HELLO," said Snufkin. "I'm glad you happened to come by. I've got a story that you might find interesting."

"I'm not one bit interested in your adventure stories tonight," muttered Sniff, and curled up into a ball.

"It's no fairy tale," said Snufkin. "It really, truly happened."

MOOMINTROLL sighed and said, "I'm afraid a lot of time will be wasted."

"And what of it?" said Snufkin. "You will dream wonderful things. And when you wake again, it will be spring…"

"ONE can never be truly free if one admires others too much," said Snufkin suddenly. "I know."

"DON'T you see? The Hattifatteners neither speak nor hear, and they see very poorly. But they are very sensitive to movement and vibrations of any kind!"

"NO need to rush now," said Snufkin soothingly. "It is dangerous to run about in the dark."

WALKING was easy because his rucksack was almost empty and he didn't have to worry about anything. Snufkin was pleased with the forest, the weather and himself. Tomorrow and yesterday were equally distant from him now, for just at that moment the bright red sun was shining down from between the birch trees, and the air was cool and mild.

The Joy of Solitude

"WHERE ARE YOU OFF TO?"
"THAT DEPENDS," SAID SNUFKIN.

"I'll come when it suits me," said an angry Snufkin. "Perhaps I shan't come at all. I just may set off in another direction entirely."

"I must take a moment to think," said Snufkin.

SNUFKIN slipped past the back of the houses and stayed in the shadows. He was as quiet as possible because he didn't want to speak to a soul.

"I live all over the place," answered Snufkin, and put the coffee pot on the fire. "Today I happen to be here; tomorrow I will be somewhere else. I wander about as I please. When I find a place I like, I pitch my tent and play my harmonica."

"Go home, little ones," Snufkin said. "You are free to go wherever you please."

"But I am not used to little children!" said Snufkin, terrified. "I don't even know if I like them."

"Well, they seem to like you!" said Little My mischievously.

"OTHER stars follow their particular orbit, like trains running along the track, but comets move around haphazardly, popping up where you least expect them," explained Moomintroll.

"Why, they are like me then!" said Snufkin with a grin. "They must be sky-wanderers."

On Remembering, Forgetting and
What is Really Important

"I forgot to write a farewell letter, I ran out of time. Oh well, all my farewell letters have been the same anyway – 'I'll be back in April. Be well', or 'I'm leaving now and shall return in the spring. Take good care of yourself'. I know that Moomintroll will understand."

And just like that, Snufkin forgot all about him.

"Oh dear," said Snufkin. "One can't always be friendly and good company. There simply isn't enough time."

"THE note!" shouted Snufkin. He carefully straightened out the paper and read it: "Please do not light a fire in the tile stove. Our ancestor is living there – Moominmamma."

MOOMINTROLL listened with his ears wide open. Then he lit the night lamp and padded over to the dresser to read Snufkin's farewell letter.

It began with the word "Hey!", written in Snufkin's big, scrawling hand. The letter itself was short: "Hey! Sleep well and don't be blue. I'll be with you again when the first day of spring arrives. Start building the dam while you are waiting – Snufkin."

No one spoke.

Then Snufkin said slowly, "It would be awful if the world exploded. It is so wonderfully splendid."

"YOU can believe
whatever you want,"
said Snufkin, blithely
peeling his banana.

"WATCH that you
don't let matters get out
of hand," said Snufkin.

On Anxiety and Conquering Your Fears

"No worries, Hemulen," said Snufkin.
"You came out all right, after all."

"I'm frightened," whispered the smallest little one, pulling on Snufkin's sleeve.

"Keep hold of me. Everything will be all right," comforted Snufkin.

"It's all over now, Sniff" said Snufkin. "Don't cry, dear friend."

"WOULD you dare to listen if I tell you something horrible?" asked Snufkin as he lit the lamp.

"How horrible?" asked the Hemulen.

"About from here to the door, perhaps even a little further," said Snufkin. "If you understand it, that is."

"By all means," said Hemulen. "Please tell me. I'll let you know if I get too frightened."

"Good," said Snufkin.

"STOP interrupting me all the time," said Snufkin. "I can see now you are much too small to listen to this kind of story. But I'll finish it just the same."

Quiet Adventures and
Wandering About

"WE SHALL HAVE TO MAKE OUR WAY BY THE SUN."

SNUFKIN made the expedition fun. He played songs on his harmonica from places far away, places that they had never heard of before.

FAR down in the valley they could just make out the narrow ribbons of the rivers and the dark outlines of the forest.

"Green trees!" said Snufkin. "Oh, how I long to be out of this stony, desolate place."

SNUFKIN wandered about southwards, stopping to pitch his tent from time to time and to let time pass. He travelled without a plan, looking about him without much thought, remembering nothing and sleeping a great deal.

SNUFKIN walked about quietly, the trees of the forest surrounding him. It began to rain. The raindrops fell on his green hat and rain jacket. The pitter-patter and rustling of the rain was everywhere and the comforting, exquisite solitude of the forest engulfed him.

MOOMINTROLL then stood on a chair and pronounced, "I want to drink a toast to the health of my good friend Snufkin, who is wandering alone towards the south as we speak. I am sure he is as happy at this moment as we are. I wish him a good place to pitch his tent, and a light heart!"

SNUFKIN was deeply interested. "Stars!" he exclaimed. "In that case, I must accompany you. I like stars more than anything else. I watch them as I fall asleep and wonder who lives on them and how to get there. The night sky looks so friendly with all those little eyes twinkling."

SNUFKIN moved nimbly, without a sound, thinking, "I find houses so disagreeable."

Silly, Precious Loved Ones

SUDDENLY, without warning, Snufkin missed the Moomin family. They could be a nuisance at times; they talked too much and they seemed to be everywhere, but even when you were with them you could somehow still be on your own.

"MY, my," thought Snufkin, continuing on his way. "He's got so many feelings, that Moomintroll... But I mustn't think of him now. I know he is a splendid Moomin, but I cannot think of him just now. Tonight I wish to be alone with my song, and tonight is not yet tomorrow."

"WAIT a moment," said Snufkin. "Did I perhaps also have – um – a mother?"

"JUST take it easy now," said Snufkin. "Sit down, Moomintroll, and tell us all about it."

MOOMINTROLL stood up and watched while Snufkin packed his tent.

"Will you be gone long?" he asked.

"No," said Snufkin. "On the first day of spring I shall return and whistle under your window. You'll see. One year goes by so quickly!"

On Ownership and Freedom

"Now you've got yourself a new piece of furniture," said Snufkin, smiling slyly, for he never understood the satisfaction others got from having things.

"I know. Everything gets so difficult if you want to own things. You have to carry them around and watch over them. I just look at them – and then when I continue on my way I can remember them in my head. I prefer that to dragging a suitcase."

"I own everything that I see and everything that pleases me. I own the entire world."

SNUFKIN picked up the hut made of spruce branches and threw it into the juniper bushes.

"That's what you should do with a house after you've lived in it," he said.

"I could do with some new trousers," said Snufkin, "but they needn't look too new. I prefer clothes that are my shape."

"WHAT a pity," said the shopkeeper. "A new hat might be in order."

But Snufkin pulled his old green hat even tighter on his head, looking alarmed. "You are very kind, but I was just thinking about how dangerous it is to get burdened with too many belongings," he said.

Sweet Melodies and
Tranquil Songs

"Maybe I shall play a while this evening,"
he thought.

SNUFKIN felt like composing a song, but he waited until the urge to do so almost overwhelmed him. Finally one night he dug out his harmonica from the bottom of his rucksack.

SNUFKIN sat in the wet moss and listened. "I have to somehow incorporate the brook into my song," he thought. "Perhaps it could be the chorus."

Suddenly a stone came loose from the dam and changed the melody of the water by an octave or so.

"How altogether lovely!" said Snufkin in admiration. "That's just how it should go."

"WHAT was that?" asked Sniff, crawling closer to the lamp.

"Nothing dangerous," said Snufkin. "Let's sing the song about the bee that got married." And he began to play.

"That was a very good song," said Moomintroll, "but it was never very clear what happened to the bee, was it? Or if the costume party was any fun."

"How about me? What could I do for you?"
asked Snufkin.

"Play me something, please!" said the Snork Maiden.

Snufkin took out his harmonica and played a few of his
most poignant songs.

Snufkin played song after song on his harmonica –
soothing dark melodies. And one after another, the little
forest creatures and the spooks of the lake all faded back
into the woods.

"Tonight is the night for a song," thought Snufkin.
"I'll think up a new song that is one part anticipation, two
parts pining for spring, and the rest a joyous declaration of
how wonderful it is to be alone and at peace with yourself."

The Songs of Snufkin

"Now I shall play a morning song," said Snufkin and he took out his harmonica. Soon everyone sang along heartily:

The night has passed and now it's day,
The Hattifatteners have rowed away.
No need to think of last night's spree,
The bright, new morning is carefree.
And on the Snork Maid's pretty head,
Curly hair will quickly spread!

SNUFKIN took out his harmonica and began to play an old song of Moomintroll's called "Every little creature has a bow upon its tail".

Little My woke up and peeked out from his pocket. She said, "Oh, I know that one!" and began to sing along in a shrill, insect-like voice:

Every little creature has a bow upon its tail.
Hemulens with flowered crowns hold garlands from the vale.
Little maiden Misabel sings, "Sadness, leave us, please,"
Whomper dances to the moon that sinks behind the trees.
Crimson tulips bloom behind the Moomin house so blue,
They wave a cheery welcome to the morning dawn and you.
The shining day is ending, time to turn in for the night,
Mymble seeks the hat she lost, the one that suits her right.

"PLAY something that I can whistle along to," yelled Moomintroll.

"How about 'Song of the Celebrant'?" suggested Snufkin.

"That one is so sad," complained the Snork Maiden.

"Well, we're going to sing it anyway," said Moomintroll. "It's got a great melody for whistling."

Snufkin played the song through and everyone joined in the final refrain:

Poor thing, you little celebrant,
  you've rejoiced until the dawn,
The morning sun is rising
  and hence the more and more you yawn.
The clock says five a.m.
  and yet you're wandering on your own,
Your little paws are tired
  and you can't find your way home.